COLOUR YOUR WAY TO BETTER FOCUS

ART FOR MINDFULNESS
WINTER WONDERLAND

PATTERNS BY LIZZIE HARPER & CHRISTINA HART-DAVIES

Harper Thorsons
An imprint of HarperCollins*Publishers*
1 London Bridge Street
London SE1 9GF
www.harpercollins.co.uk

First published by HarperCollins*Publishers* in 2015
1 3 5 7 9 10 8 6 4 2

Patterns by Lizzie Harper & Christina Hart-Davies
Introduction text by Imi Lo

A catalogue record for this book is available from the British Library

ISBN 978-0-00-794921-2

Printed and bound in China

Introduction

Mindfulness has become extremely popular in recent years, as scientists discover more about the wide array of benefits it has to offer—reducing stress, increasing joy, enhancing emotional intelligence, and undoing bad habits. Although it can be defined in various ways, mindfulness is most simply described as approaching the present moment non-judgementally, and with curiosity. It offers a break from our incessant, autopilot mind, and provides the opportunity to live a fuller life.

Despite urban myth, mindfulness practise is not simply about sitting uncomfortably, or chanting "Omm". *Art for Mindfulness* lies in the intersection of mindfulness and therapeutic art, offering a doorway into mindfulness that is accessible, relatable, and fun. Feeling burdened by the chaos of modern life, many adults have found that colouring helps them reconnect with a simpler, more spontaneous way of being.

In order to reap the most benefits from this book, I would invite you to approach it with a playful and curious attitude. A few partially coloured-in patterns follow for use as inspiration before you embark on your own work. However, despite what your art teacher may have told you in school, there is absolutely no right or wrong way of colouring. You may be pleasantly surprised by the outcome when you trust your instinct and allow colour and strokes to naturally unfold; you may discover a deep sense of calm when you begin to pay the activity your full attention. You may also find this to be a great way to develop more soulful connections with those around you. I hope that you not only enjoy this book, but also discover a deeper layer of spiritual practise through immersing in the art of mindful colouring.

Imi Lo (UKCP, HCPC, MMH), Art Psychotherapist and Mindfulness Teacher

"Concentration is the ground of happiness. If you live twenty-four hours a day in mindfulness and concentration, one day is a lot."

Thích Nhất Hạnh

“The snow goose need not bathe to make itself white. Neither need you do anything than be yourself.”

Lao-Tzu

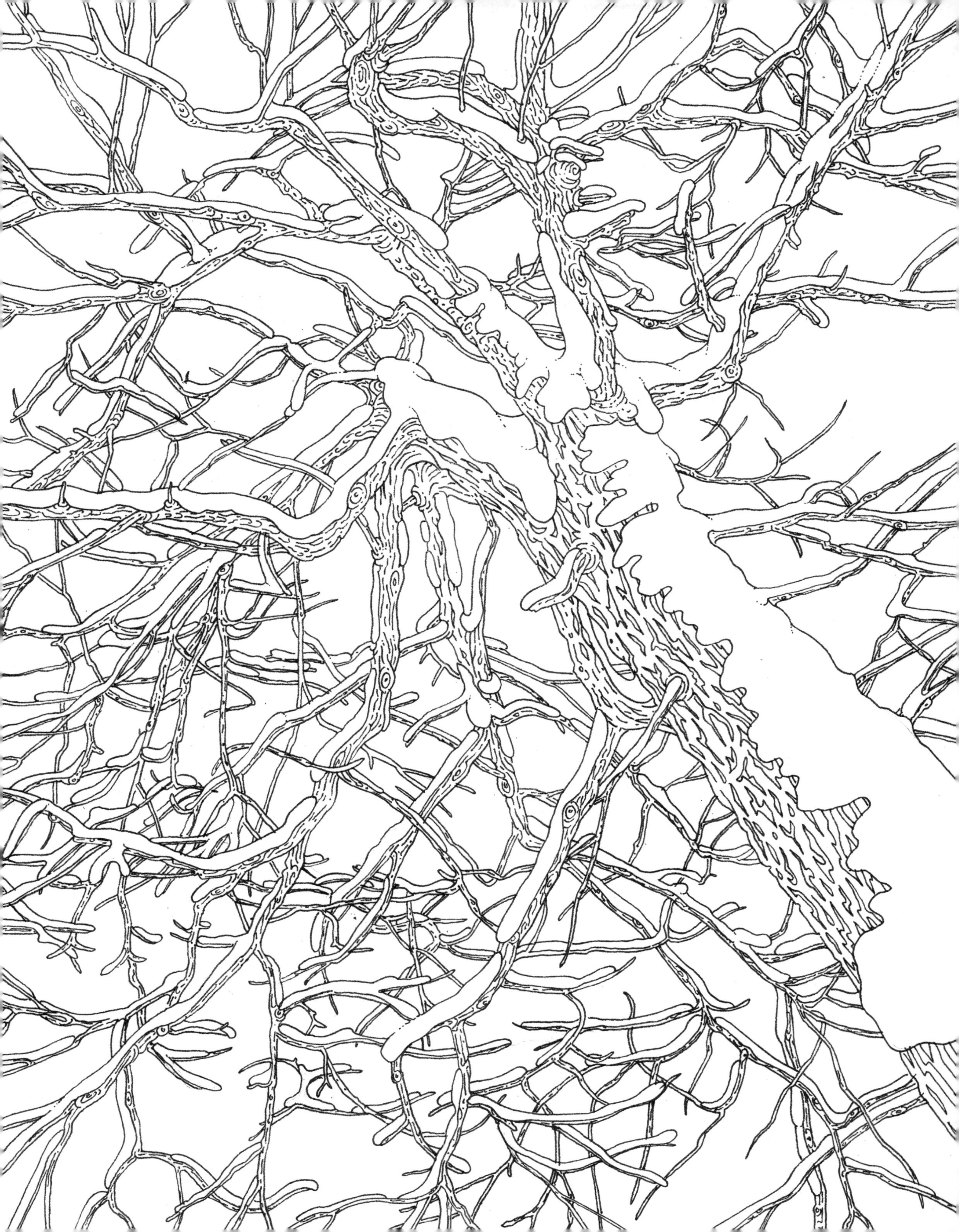

“Mindfulness can be summed up in two words: pay attention. Once you notice what you’re doing, you have the power to change it.”

Michelle Burford

"Begin doing what you want to do now. We are not living in eternity. We have only this moment, sparkling like a star in our hand—and melting like a snowflake."

Francis Bacon

“A life is like a garden.
Perfect moments can be had, but not preserved, except in memory.”

Leonard Nimoy

“Change your opinions, keep to your principles; change your leaves, keep intact your roots.”

Victor Hugo

"When consciously and kindly focusing awareness on life as it unfolds minute by precious minute, you are better able to savor each experience."

Sue Patton Thoele

“Looking at beauty in the world is the first step of purifying the mind.”

Amit Ray

"Mindfulness of oneself cultivates wisdom. Mindfulness of others cultivates compassion."

Stonepeace

“Mindfulness simply means being aware, being present. When you are breathing and know that you are breathing, that is mindfulness of breathing.”

Soren Gordhamer

“You can’t use up creativity. The more you use, the more you have.”

Maya Angelou

“What we get from each moment depends on the attention we give it, and the quality of our experience reflects the quality of our awareness.”

Roger Walsh

**“Everything is created twice,
first in the mind and then in reality.”**

Robin S. Sharma

“Each place is the right place—the place where I now am can be a sacred space.”

Ravi Ravindra

“Let the breath lead the way.”

Sharon Salzberg

“Most of us take for granted that time flies, meaning that it passes too quickly. But in the mindful state, time doesn’t really pass at all. There is only a single instant of time that keeps renewing itself over and over with infinite variety.”

Deepak Chopra

“Through recognizing and realizing the empty essence, instead of being selfish and self-centered, one feels very open and free.”

Tsoknyi Rinpoche

“When you reach a calm and quiet meditative state, that is when you can hear the sound of silence.”

Stephen Richards

fresh cut
CHRISTMAS TREES

"I have found my greatest moments of joy and peace just sitting in silence, and then I take that joy and peace with me out into the world."

Holly Mosier

“We need never be bound by the limitations of our previous or current thinking, nor are we ever locked into being the person we used to be, or think we are.”

Allan Lokos

“Stop, breathe, look around, and embrace the miracle of each day, the miracle of life.”

Jeffrey A. White

“Hold to the now, the here, through which all future plunges to the past.”

James Joyce

“Creativity is putting your imagination to work, and it’s produced the most extraordinary results in human culture.”

Ken Robinson

“Like a child standing in a beautiful park with his eyes shut tight, there’s no need to imagine trees, flowers, deer, birds, and sky; we merely need to open our eyes and realize what is already here, who we already are.”

Bo Lozoff

**“Time is the coin of your life.
It is the only coin you have, and only
you can determine how it will be spent.
Be careful lest you let other people
spend it for you.”**

Carl Sandburg

"Try to be mindful, and let things take their natural course. Then your mind will become still in any surroundings, like a clear forest pool. All kinds of wonderful, rare animals will come to drink at the pool, and you will clearly see the nature of all things. You will see many strange and wonderful things come and go, but you will be still."

Ajahn Chah

“Through loving kindness, everyone and everything can flower again from within.”

Sharon Salzberg

**“When mind knows,
we call it knowledge.
When heart knows,
we call it love.
And when being knows,
we call it meditation.”**

Osho

“Those who are awake live in a constant state of amazement.”

Jack Kornfield

“People are at their most mindful when they are at play. If we find ways of enjoying our work, blurring the lines between work and play, the gains will be greater.”

Ellen Langer

“Love the moment, and the energy of that moment will spread beyond all boundaries.”

Corita Kent

“There’s nowhere you can be that isn’t where you’re meant to be . . .”

John Lennon

"Study how water flows in a valley stream, smoothly and freely between the rocks. Everything— even mountains, rivers, plants, and trees—should be your teacher."

Morehei Ueshiba

“Do not encumber your mind with useless thoughts. What good does it do to brood on the past or anticipate the future? Remain in the simplicity of the present moment.”

Dilgo Khyentse

“Old ways won’t open new doors.”

Miroslav Rajkovic

**“Every child is an artist,
the problem is staying an artist
when you grow up.”**

Pablo Picasso

NOEL
Santa
Rudolph

“Yesterday I was clever, so I wanted to change the world. Today I am wise, so I am changing myself.”

Rumi

"Doing nothing is better than being busy doing nothing."

Lao-Tzu

"I would love to live as a river flows, carried by the surprise of its own unfolding."

John O'Donohue

**“Be kind whenever possible.
It is always possible.”**

The Dalai Lama

“Today stretches ahead of you, waiting to be shaped. You are the sculptor who gets to do the shaping. What today will be like is up to you.”

Steve Maraboli

“The key is to trust your heart to move where your unique talents can flourish. This old world will really spin when work becomes a joyous expression of the soul.”

Al Sacharov

“Try pausing right before and right after undertaking a new action, even something simple like putting a key in a lock to open a door. Such pauses take a brief moment, yet they have the effect of decompressing time and centering you.”

David Steindl-Rast

"The basic root of happiness lies in our minds; outer circumstances are nothing more than adverse or favorable."

Matthieu Ricard

“Curiosity about life in all of its aspects, I think, is still the secret of great creative people.”

Leo Burnett

"It is better to have enough ideas for some of them to be wrong, than to be always right by having no ideas at all."

Edward de Bono

“Always hold fast to the present. Every situation, indeed every moment, is of infinite value, for it is the representative of a whole eternity.”

Johann Wolfgang von Goethe

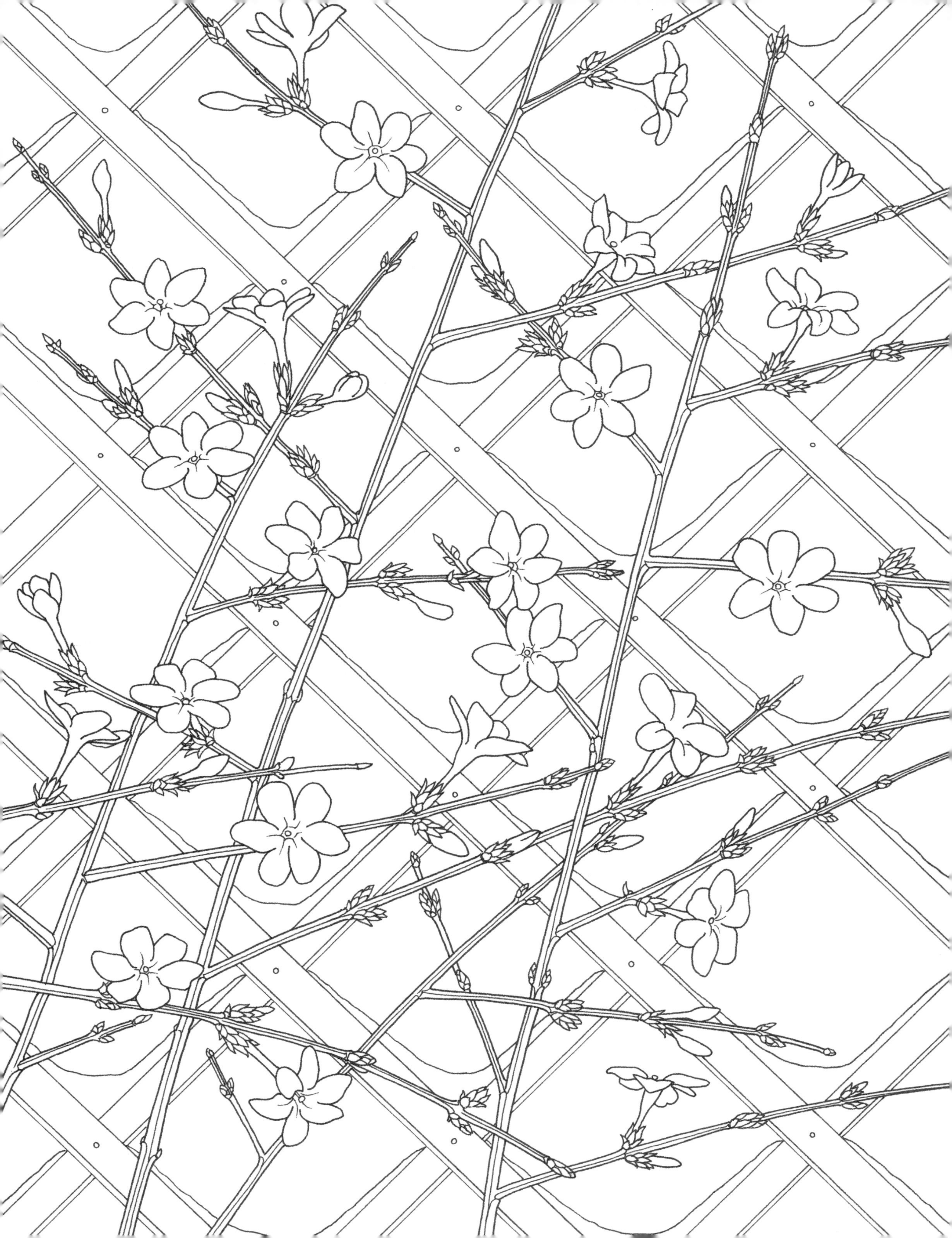

“We can always begin again.”

Jack Kornfield

“You should sit in meditation for 20 minutes a day— unless you’re too busy—then you should sit for an hour.”

Old Zen adage

“Feelings come and go like clouds in a windy sky. Conscious breathing is my anchor.”

Thích Nhất Hạnh

"Meditation is the only intentional, systematic human activity which at bottom is about not trying to improve yourself or get anywhere else, but simply to realize where you already are."

Jon Kabat-Zinn

“The flowering of love is meditation.”

Jiddu Krishnamurti

“An invasion of armies can be resisted, but not an idea whose time has come.”

Victor Hugo

**“To live a creative life,
we must lose our fear of being wrong.”**

Joseph Chilton Pierce

**“World is a dance.
Mindfulness is witnessing that dance.”**

Amit Ray

“One who is patient glows with an inner radiance.”

Allan Lokos

“Creativity requires the courage to let go of certainties.”

Erich Fromm

"I wish that life should not be cheap, but sacred. I wish the days to be as centuries, loaded, fragrant."

Ralph Waldo Emerson

“Creativity is allowing oneself to make mistakes. Art is knowing which ones to keep.”

Scott Adams

“Life is trying things to see if they work.”

Ray Bradbury

BAKERY
10